For the Winkies, and all the Winkies' Winkies

Also by Steve Bell
Bell's Eye
Unspeakable If...
Unstoppable If...
If...Marches On
My Vision For A New You

by Steve Bell and Brian Homer
Chairman Blair's Little Red Book

IF... BURSTS OUT

Steve Bell

To Eva
with very best wishes
Steve Bell

Jonathan Cape
London

Published by Jonathan Cape 2010

2 4 6 8 10 9 7 5 3 1

First published in Great Britain in 2010 by
Jonathan Cape, Random House, 20 Vauxhall Bridge Road, London SW1V 2SA

www.rbooks.co.uk

Addresses for companies within The Random House Group Limited can be found at:
www.randomhouse.co.uk/offices.htm

The Random House Group Limited Reg. No. 954009

A CIP catalogue record for this book is available from the British Library

ISBN 9780224087629

The Random House Group Limited makes every effort to ensure that the papers used in its books are made from trees that have been legally sourced from well-managed and credibly certified forests. Our paper procurement policy can be found at:
www.randomhouse.co.uk/paper.htm

Design by Homer Creative. Printed and bound in China by C&C Offset Printing Co., Ltd

Contents

In February 2006…

In February 2006 when our story begins cartoons, unusually, were at the top of the news agenda. The fatwa against the Danish cartoonists who had dared to draw the Prophet Mohammed in an edition of *Jyllands-Posten* some six months earlier, had led to cartoon demonstrations, cartoon riots and even cartoon deaths. This proved an awkward moment for cartoonists across the world. Innocent scribbling men and women, sitting at their desks, were asked how they felt about it. They were united in one thought: on the whole they would prefer not to have their heads sawn off, on video or not, thank you very much. As demands for respect for people's religious sensibilities increased in stridency, it became harder to assert the equally important human right to take the piss. Some of us also had the added problem of having several hundred previous offences to be taken into consideration.

"I am the Jesus Christ of politics."

Silvio Berlusconi, 11 February 2006

8

9

11

13

14

15

16

17

GROUNDHOG WAR

"WE WILL FIGHT THEM IN IRAQ..."

"WE WILL FIGHT THEM ACROSS THE WORLD..."

"WE WILL STAY AND FIGHT UNTIL THE FIGHT HAS BEEN WON..."

MARS

EARTH

GROUNDHOG WAR

"WE WILL FIGHT THEM IN IRAQ..."

GROUNDHOG WARS

THIS IS NOT A CLASH OF CIVILISATIONS. THIS IS A CLASH ABOUT CIVILISATION

...IT IS THE AGE-OLD BATTLE BETWEEN PROGRESS AND REACTION.

THEIR ATTITUDE TO AMERICA IS ABSURD, THEIR CONCEPT OF GOVERNANCE PRE-FEUDAL, THEIR POSITIONS ON WOMEN AND OTHER FAITHS REACT-IONARY AND REGRESSIVE

GROUNDHOG WARS

THIS IS NOT A CLASH OF CIVILISATIONS. THIS IS A CLASH ABOUT CIVILISATION

19

ARE THERE ANY **FURTHER QUESTIONS** ABOUT MY **BUDGET**?

ACCORDING TO YOUR FIGURES THERE WILL BE **ONE YEAR** OF VERY **SLIGHT FISCAL LOOSENING** FOLLOWED BY **TWO YEARS** OF FISCAL **TIGHTENING**. WOULD YOU AGREE WITH THAT ANALYSIS, CHANCELLOR?

I WOULD **NOT** NECESSARILY **DEMUR** FROM THAT VIEW. ANY **FURTHER POINTS**?

WHAT'S THAT NEXT TO YOU?

IT'S AN **ENORMOUS PILE OF POONDS**. WHY DO YOU ASK?

MR BROWN — NEXT TO THAT **PILE OF POONDS**...

...WHAT'S **THAT THING** ON YOUR FACE?

THIS THING IS MY **NEW SMILE**...

THE PILE OF POONDS IS AN APPROXIMATE REPRESENTATION OF THE **COST OF ORTHO-DONTIC TREATMENT**.

I'M CRYIN' INSIDE, Y'KNOW

20

21

23

May 2006

"Its not the size of the dog in the fight, its the size of the fight in the dog."

Mark Twain

©Steve Bell 2006 - 2387 30.5.06 -

25

28

29

I'M 'ERE AS A **DISINTERESTED THIRD PARTY** ANIMAL....

24·5·5924·

...TO **BROKER** A STABLE AND ORDERLY **TRANSITION**

NO YOU'RE NOT...

YOU'RE HERE AS A **USELESS MUTT** TO BROKER A **KICK UP THE ARSE!**

© STEVE BELL 2006.

?

THE DEPUTY PRIME MINISTER EXISTS AND HAS BEEN FED

WHAT'S THE **FOOKIN'** POINT?

25·5·5925· © Steve Bell '06

NOBODY SHOWS ME ANY **RESPECT.** I COULDN'T BROKER A **PISS UP** IN A **BREWERY**

CHEER UP JOHN!

THINK OF ALL YOUR ACHIEVEMENTS

31

WELCOME TO THE **LAME DUCK SUMMIT**!

29·5·2926·

WE'RE GONNA PLUG OURSELVES SOME **LAME DUCKS**

PULL!!

©Steve Bell 2006

BLAMMO

I NEED A **HOLIDAY**!

30·5·5927

NO YOU **DON'T** — YOU NEED **THERAPY**!

UH OH!

©Steve Bell 2006·

NO! NO!!

YES! YES!! A MEXICAN SHIT BATH!

IT'S THE **ONLY WAY** YOU'LL GET IN TOUCH WITH YOUR **INJURED INNER FOWL**!

33

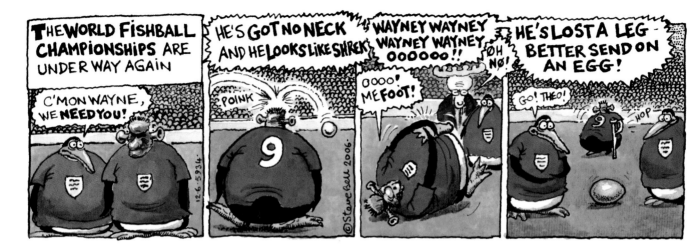

THE EGG IS UNMARKED IN THE BOX

ON ME 'EAD!

14·6·5936·

IT'S SCORED!

THE CELEBRATIONS BEGIN....

...AND END

BUGGER!

SPLUT

THE FABULOUS PARROTS ARE A BIT OFF COLOUR

YOU GOT ANY PIES?

MOVE AROUND MORE!

HAS ANYBODY GOT A PIE? I'M TIRED

15·6·5937 © Steve Bell '06

BUT IT DOESN'T SEEM TO MATTER...

IT'S ALL IN THE WAY KAKA TIMES HIS RUNS *

CRISPS! I NEED CRISPS!

* SIC – THANKS TO BILL

37

38

39

THE 'OLE COUNTRY'S GOIN' TO THE DOGS

PRIME MINISTER IS AVAILABLE

'ERE, MARKET — TWENTY QUID SAYS YOU BEAT TONY TO THE BIG OFF!

AVAILABLE

I'LL GIVE YOU THE BIG OFF! CLEAR OFF OR I'LL BITE YER ARSE!

KABOOM

HOWDY PARDNER! I KINDA LIKE THE LOOK O' YOUR DAWGHOUSE!

THE DEPUTY PRIME MINISTER IS AVAILABLE

I CAN PICTURE IT — A MEGA CASINO, FIVE HUNDRED FEET TALL, DOMINATING THE THAMES GATEWAY! YOU COULD WEAR A UNIFORM AND SELL TICKETS...

©Steve Bell 2006

...BUT NO SEX, PLEASE, I'M A SOUTHERN BAPTIST!

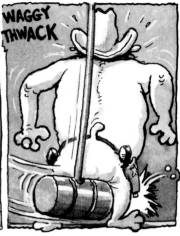

41

September 2006

"So while Conservatives may think that youth, inexperience, and naivete are the answer to their problems, I say they are not the answer to the country's problems."

Sir Menzies Campbell MP

GO HOME TO YOUR CONSTITUENCIES AND PREPARE FOR DEATH...

LIBERAL DEMOCRATS

TRIDENT - QUITE POSSIBLY

43

44

MR BLAH — A FRIENDLY WORD OF ADVICE...

...FACK ORFFF AND TAKE YOUR ILL-BRED SLUT OF A WIFE WITH YOU...

I PLEDGE HERE AND NOW...

...THAT I WILL NEVER DARKEN THESE DOORS AGAIN

AND I'VE CRAPPED IN THE WARDROBE!

©Steve Bell '06

SO THE FAREWELL TOUR IS UNDERWAY AT LAST...

HOW D'YOU FEEL?

MUCH BETTER FOR KNOWING THAT YOU CRAPPED IN THE WARDROBE AT BALMORAL

WHAT WERE YOU THINKING OF??

WHAT'S THE POINT OF BURNING YER BOATS IF YOU CAN'T LEAVE A BAD SMELL BEHIND??

©Steve Bell 2006

AT LEAST WE WON'T HAVE TO MINGLE WITH THOSE HORSE-FACED UPPER CLASS TWATS ANYMORE

WHAT ABOUT MY EARLDOM?

45

46

47

48

CHARLES — YOU'RE GOOD AT **JOKES**!...

...I THINK I NEED A **STRAIGHT MAN**

WHAT ARE YE **SAYIN'**, MONG?

...**NO, NO**, I JUST NEED SOMEONE TO HELP ME **DELIVER MY MATERIAL** WHO CAN **KEEP A STRAIGHT FACE**

ARE YOUSE CALLIN' ME A **POOOF**?

20.9.5964

— © Steve Bell 2006.

GORDON BROWN?

- 21.9.5965 -

DON'T TALK TO ME ABOUT **GORDON BROWN**!! I TAUGHT HIM **EVERYTHING HE KNOWS**!

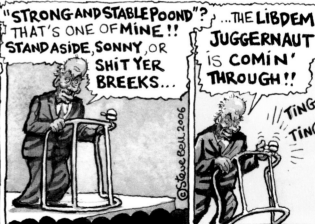

"**STRONG AND STABLE POOND**"? THAT'S ONE OF **MINE**!! STAND ASIDE, SONNY, OR **SHIT YER BREEKS**...

© Steve Bell 2006

...THE LIBDEM JUGGERNAUT IS COMIN' THROUGH!!

TING TING

MANCHESTER...

25.9.5966

THE EYEBALL IS CLOSING!

LONG LIVE THE ARSE!

© Steve Bell 2006

HAIL MIGHTY SEAT!!

NOTHING CAN WITHSTAND THE ARSE!!

HAIL GREAT WIND OF NO CHANGE!

IT IS A FAR FAR BETTER THING THAT I DO NOW...

26.9.5967

...THAN I HAVE EVER DONE.

IT IS A FAR FAR BETTER PLACE THAT I GO TO THAN I HAVE EVER KNOWN.

© Steve Bell 2006.

IT IS A FAR FAR BIGGER ARSE THAT SUCCEEDS ME THAN HAS EVER BEEN WIPED.

50

51

52

53

October 2006

"Let sunshine win the day."

David Cameron, 1st October 2006

55

56

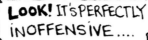

58

OK DONUTT, I **RESPECT** EVERYTHING YOU SAY...

...WE ALL HAVE A RIGHT TO OUR **OPINIONS**, BUT, DAMMIT — YOU'RE **HEAD OF THE ARMY!**

YOU **SPOKE OPENLY** TO THE **MEDIA**, FOR HEAVEN'S SAKE!

©Steve Bell 2006-

SURELY YOU COULD **AT LEAST** HAVE WORN A **VEIL?**

SORRY, PM, WE **DON'T DO VEILS**...

...WE DO **BALACL- -AVAS**, THOUGH!

I DON'T KNOW WHAT YOU DO TO THE **ENEMY**, GENERAL...

...BUT YOU MAKE ME **BLOODY UNCOMFORTABLE**

-©Steve Bell 2006-

59

THE **CAMELS ARE** GETTIN' RESTLESS, SARGE!

-23·10·5982-

THAT'S BECAUSE THEY'RE **ITCHIN'** TO BE INTERFERED WITH, KID.

BUT SARGE!

NO BUTS, KID. WE CAME HERE TO FUCK THOSE CAMELS INTO THE **TWENTY FIRST CENTURY...**

...SO **THAT'S WHAT WE'RE GONNA DO**

DOWN! DOWN!!

_24·10·5983_

DOWN!! SARGE! WHAT IS IT?

I CAN'T BELIEVE **THIS**: THE CAMELS...

©SteveBell'06

...THE CAMELS ARE FUCKING **THEMSELVES!**

SPFFFRRLLT

WHEEEE

61

COMPLETE IRAQIFACIFICATION INSIDE 12-18 MONTHS!!

30.10.5986.

YOU'RE TALKIN' OUTA YOUR ASS!!

ELECTOR'S VOICE

FORWARD WITH THE IRAQI PEOPLE!

MAJOR COMBAT ACTIVITY IS OVER AND OVER AGAIN!

© Steve Bell 2006~

WE WILL STAY UNTIL THE JOB IS DONE...

31.10.5987. ©Steve Bell 2006.

PRESIDENT of the UNITED STATES

...UNTIL THE HANDOVER TO A FULLY FREEMAN MOXIFIED....

...IRAQIFACIFICATED IRAQ IS COMPLETE.

READ MY LIPS— —NO CUT AND RUN!

64

65

November 2006

"*Guardian* newspaper? Well, I don't read that paper often."

George Bush, 17 November 2006

69

70

72

RIGHT, YOU LITTLE 'ORRORS-- THIS IS THE ATOMIC WEAPONS ESTABLISHMENT.

29-11-6004

...IN ALDERMASTON, WHERE THE GOVERNMENT HAS THOUGHTFULLY BOUGHT YOU A COMPULSORY TIMESHARE!!

©Steve Bell 2006

LOOK--THEY'RE INVESTING IN LOTS OF NEW NUCLEAR WEAPONS OF MASS DESTRUCTION JUST FOR YOU TO USE ANYTIME YOU LIKE (PROVIDING YOU CAN GET IN WITHOUT BEING SHOT ON SIGHT)!

BABY I LOVE THE WAY YOU ARE...

29-11-6005-

...YOU EXUDE THE RELAXED CONFIDENCE OF SOMEONE WHO'S BEEN AROUND...

"CLANK"

...AND WHEN YOUR BITS START FALLING OFF I FIND YOU EVEN HARDER TO RESIST!

©Steve Bell '06

73

74

KNOCK KNOCK

-6.12.6008-

WHO'S THERE?

THE MAN FROM ULTIMATE INSURANCE ™ ®

IN THIS UNCERTAIN WORLD WE AT ULTIMATE ™ ® BELIEVE THAT ASSURED SUICIDE ™ ® SHOULD BE AVAILABLE TO ALL....

...REGARDLESS OF THE WHIMS OF THE U.S.A!

GOTTLE O' GEER

©Steve Bell 2006

YOU SEE, I LIKE TO THINK OF MYSELF AS A BRIDGE....

7.12.6009 ©Steve Bell 2006

...BETWEEN THE WILDER SHORES OF THE USA AND THE RATHER STUFFY CONFINES OF OLD EUROPE...

SLURP

...ABLE TO LEND A RESTRAINING HAND AND WISE COUNSEL THAT MAY ACTUALLY BE LISTENED TO....

GLUG GLUG

...WHILST MAINTAINING A RATIONAL AND CONSIDERED INDEPENDENCE FROM BOTH SIDES

76

January 2007

"There are not enough Indians in the world to defeat the Seventh Cavalry."

General George Armstrong Custer

82

84

YOU THINK THIS IS ALL TO DO WITH **DOGS**, DON'T YOU? I CAN TELL BY THE **LOOK** IN YOUR EYE!

BUT IT'S **NOTHING** TO DO WITH **DOGS**. IT'S ALL ABOUT **HARD POWER!**

THE **ONLY THING** THE BRITISH PEOPLE RESPECT IS **HARD POWER**. YOU'D BETTER **BELIEVE IT!**

LASH

THWACK

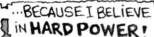

I'VE NEVER TAKEN A **SOFT OPTION** IN MY LIFE...

...BECAUSE I BELIEVE IN **HARD POWER!**

ASBOS FOR TERRORISTS BEFORE THEY'VE EVEN HAD A CHANCE TO **BECOME TERRORISTS**...

...THAT'S POWER **SO HARD** IT'LL **RUPTURE** YOUR INSIDES!!

18·1·6025·

86

87

88

91

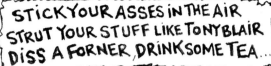

94

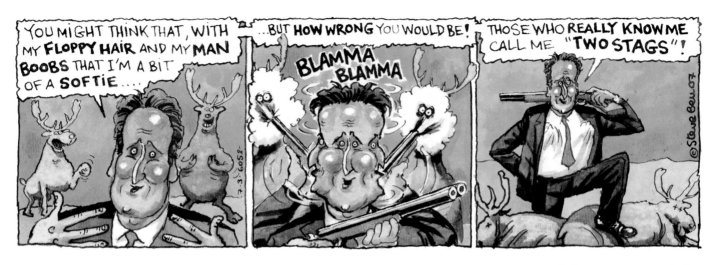

96

97

March 2007

"Tony Blair is one of the finest comic actors of his generation."

Catherine Tate, March 2007

99

CAMBO

© Steve Bell 2007
-26·3·6062-

WE GODDA GED OUR GUYS OUDA IRAN AN' BACK IN IRAQ WHERE THEY BELONG!

DO WE GET TO **KILL GOOKS** YET?

SURE, LI'L BUDDY... **OH MY GAHD!!!** MY T-SHIRT IS **WET!**

WHERE ARE WE, CAMBO?

-27·3·6063

© Steve Bell 07

CAN I DISEMBOWEL ANYONE YET?

NOT YET, LI'L BUDDY— WE'RE UP SHATT-AL-ARAB WITHOUT A PEDALO!

SHAK'LIK

100

104

106

BAMBI THE FINAL HOURS 2

ARE YOU **STILL HERE** ?

JA?

SO, YOU **BURN ZE HAUS DOWN** MIT YOUR FUNERAL PYRE YET YOU PERSIST IN **HIDEOUS AFTER LIFE** ?

UND YOUR POINT IS??

ALLE IST SCHEISS!

BAMBI THE FINAL HOURS 2

CHITTER CHITTER CHEE CHEE ARE **YOU SE** LOOKIN' AT ME??

PORPOISE! WHAT IS IT, OLD FRIEND?

ARE YOU... ...**UNFIT**?

NO, NO THEY A' SAID AH WIS A **USELESS WEE JOBBIE!**

BUT **AH SHOWED 'EM** — AH HAD **NINE WEE JOBBIES** IN **TEN YEARS!**

TOMORROW IN BAGHDAD, EH HEN?

COUGH GAG

BAMBI THE FINAL HOURS 2
©Steve Bell 07

ZIS IST YOUR **DEER FÜHRER** BROADCASTING TO YOU FROM ZE HOT SMOULDERING WRECKAGE OF ZE **STAG REICH**...

..YOU KNOW, ZIS IS **NOT ZE TIME FÜR SOUNDEN BITE ZENS**....

...BUT **TODAY** I FEEL ZE **HOOVES OF HISTORY** ON MEIN SHOULDER!

BAMBI THE FINAL HOURS THE **DIRECTOR'S CUT**

IT IS A **FAR FAR BETTER THING** ZAT I DO NOW ZAN I HAF EFFER DONE...

YOU CAN **SAY ZAT** AGAIN!

IT IS A **FAR FAR BETTER PLACE** ZAT I GO TO ZAN I HAF EFFER KNOWN!

FORK OFF TO FORFAR, MEIN FÜHRER!

I VAS A **FAR FAR BETTER FÜHRER** ZAN YOU FARQUARS EVER DESERVED!

BEHOLD ZE **HEAD** OF A CUDDLY TOYRANT!

©Steve Bell 2007

110

111

112

113

TWENTY FIVE YEARS AGO YOU LOYALLY PERFORMED YOUR DUTY...

.13·6·6092·

HAD YOU NOT DONE SO THEN, WE WOULD ALL NOW BE SPEAKING ALBATROSS!

©Steve Bell '07

AAAAARRKK!! AAAAAAAAARRK!

POP!

PHTHRRRRP

I STAND ATOP THIS PILE OF BRAVE, DEAD PENGUINS...

14·6·6093 ©Steve Bell '07

...LOOKING AT AN EVEN BIGGER PILE OF BRAVE, COWERING WHIPPED CUR DEAD ALBATROSS...

...AND I FEEL PROUD, AND NOT A LITTLE HUMBLED TO SAY THAT EVERY ONE OF THEM DIED TO HELP PRESERVE MY POLITICAL CAREER AND THUS THE FUTURE OF CIVILISATION. GOD SAVE THE QUEEN!

June 2007

"Let the work of change begin."

Gordon Brown, June 2007

-©Steve Bell 2007 - 2544 · 28·6·07 -

118

121

122

124

125

126

128

BROWN GUY — WELCOME TO AMERICA....

LET'S WALK THIS WAY...

30.7.6118 ©Steve Bell '07

BROWN GUY — I COULDN'T LET YOU LEAVE HERE...

...WITHOUT TAKIN' YOU FOR A RIDE ON **GOLF CART ONE!**

BUT I DON'T PLAY GOLF!

31.7.6119 ©Steve Bell 2007

NEITHER DO I, BROWN GUY!

PARP PARP!

♪

MISTER GORDON BROWN GUY IS A FUNNY GUY...

...HE CRACKS ME UP WHEN HE WAGGLES HIS BIG OL' EARS!

OUR VARLUES ARE SHARED MUTUAL VARLUES...

MR PRESIDENT MAKES ME SMILE WHEN HE NODS HIS HEAD AND JINGLES HIS LITTLE BELL!

TING·A·LING

©Steve Bell '07

THIS IS THE GREATEST HUMANITARIAN DISASTER THE WORLD FACES TODAY...

2·8·6121-

OVER 650,000 PEOPLE DEAD, MORE THAN FOUR MILLION PEOPLE DISPLACED, IRAAA....
...I BEG YOUR PARDON, STATISTICAL BLIP...

200,000 DEAD, OVER TWO MILLION PEOPLE DISPLACED...

©Steve Bell 2007-

...THE SITUATION IN DARFUR IS A CONTIN-UING AFFRONT TO OUR SHARED VARLUES...

FLASHBACK TO THE SIXTIES: ATTEN-HUT! YOUNG-GEORGE DUBYA BUSH REPORTIN' FOR DUTY, SAH!!

I INTEND TO GO TO 'NAM AND STAY THERE TILL THE JOB IS DONE, SAH!

WHISKEY

BUT FIRST I HAVE TO DRINK THIS BOOZE AND SNORT THESE DRUGS, SAH!

GOOD LUCK SON - YOU'LL NEED IT!!

FOR YOUNG GEORGE W. TIME PASSES, ELASTICALLY...

LEFT

RIGHT

LEFT

RIGHT

ATTEN-GLUG!

WHISKEY

BAD NEWS GEORGE - LIBERAL DEFEATISTS ARE THREATENIN' THE WAR EFFORT IN 'NAM!

©Steve Bell '07

September 2007

"And he said unto them that stood by, Take from him the pound, and give it to him that hath ten pounds."

Luke, Chapter 19, verse 24

137

AN INSTITUTION SOMEWHERE IN THE HOME COUNTIES:

BARONESS THATCHER...

10.9. 6130-

COULD YOU TELL ME WHO THE PRIME MINISTER IS?

GORDON BROWN IS THE PRIME MINISTER.

THANK YOU BARONESS...

I AM GORDON BROWN!

BARONESS?

I AM GORDON BROWN!

LISTEN TO THE BAG!

-11.9. 6131-

FEEL MY BIG CLUNKING HUG!!

PANIC ALARM

©Steve Bell 2007

138

140

WELCOME TO **BOURNEMOCKBA**

WE MUST EMBRACE NEW FORMS OF PARTICIPATION...

WE WILL HAVE CONTINUOUS POLICY DISCUSSIONS INVOLVING THE WHOLE PARTY (ME)

— ©Steve Bell 2007 · 24·9·6138 —

WHY IS IT THAT A **POOR, DEPRIVED STAKEHOLDER LADY,** LIVING IN PERTHSHIRE...

...HAVE **NO SAY** IN THE GREAT POLICY DECISIONS BEFORE US, WHILE **HORSE-TRADING, HAND-WAVING DELEGATES** HERE AT THE SEASIDE ARE **ALLOWED TO SPEAK** IN HER PLACE?

25·9·6139 ©Steve Bell 2007

I SWEAR UPON THE BONES OF OUR FORMER LEADER THAT **EVERYONE** SHALL HAVE AN EQUAL OPPORTUNITY TO **SAY AS LITTLE AS THEY LIKE!**

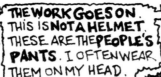

146

147

148

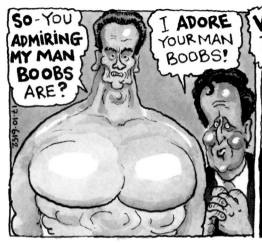

SO-YOU ADMIRING MY MAN BOOBS ARE?

I ADORE YOUR MAN BOOBS!

VELL! SHIRT AUF!! I VILL ADVISE YOU ON MANBOOB POLICY!

OOH-YES PLEASE!

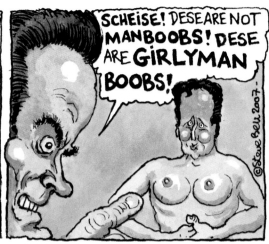

SCHEISE! DESE ARE NOT MANBOOBS! DESE ARE GIRLYMAN BOOBS!

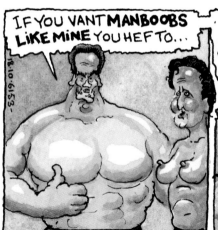

IF YOU VANT MANBOOBS LIKE MINE YOU HEF TO...

...EAT VON COW A DAY, ALL ZE VALNUTS YOU CAN CRECK MIT YOUR EYELIDS....

...PLUS A BIG HEALTHY BOWL OF STEROIDS!

MMMM!

HOW YOU FEEL NOW?

HIMMEL!

150

TONY – ONE SMALL THING – THIS **COVER PICTURE**....

MY PET GOAT
–THE INSIDE STORY

TONY BLAIR

31·10·6156·

...KINDA MAKES IT LOOK LIKE I'M **GIVIN' IT TO YOU UP THE ASS**. AM I RIGHT?

NO!

NO NO NO NO!! IT SIMPLY DEPICTS THE FACT THAT YOU'RE **BEHIND ME 100 PERCENT!**

OKAY – BUT JUST REMEMBER **WHO'S PAYIN' YOUR WAGES!**

THE AMERICAN PEOPLE, SIR, GOD BLESS 'EM!

MY PET GOAT
–THE INSIDE STORY

I GOT **ANOTHER PROBLEM** WITH YOUR BOOK, TONY...

THE INSIDE STORY OF THE RELATIONSHIP THAT ROCKED THE WORLD

NOW IT CAN BE TOLD IN E·Z·READ FORMAT

MY PET GOAT
–THE INSIDE STORY

TONY BLAIR

...THERE **AIN'T NOTHIN'** IN IT. NO WRITIN', NO PICTURES, DIDDLY **SQUAT**...

DON'T WORRY – – IT'S HIGH UP ON MY **"TO DO"** LIST

T. BLAIR'S TO DO LIST

1 BRING PEACE TO MIDDLE EAST

2 GET TOUGH WITH IRAN

3 WRITE GRAPHIC NOVEL ABOUT MY STRUGGLE

4 FIND GHOST WRITER/ARTIST

YOU WANT ME TO **GHURST** WRITE AND DRUR YOUR MEMOIRS? SHOW ME THE **MONNAIE**, M'SIEUR BLAIR!

November 2007

"And they said unto him, Lord,
he hath ten pounds."

Luke, Chapter 19, verse 25

MR STRAW — ARE YOU **ECTUALLY A MEM-BER** OF THE **HICE OF LORDS?**

· 5·11·6158·

I **CAN'T ACCEPT** THE GRACIOUS SPEECH FROM A **NON-MEMBER**.

©Steve Bell '07

WALKING **BECKWARDS** IMPRESSES ME **NOT ONE JOT!** YOU NEED A **HET** WITH **BALLS ON!!**

YOU'RE **NOT LORD CHAUNCELLOR,** STRAW! YOU'RE A **BLEDDY MINISTER OF JUSTICE!** DO AS THE MONARCH **SAYS...**

· 6·11·6159·

YOU'RE NOT A **MIMBER** OF THE **HICE OF LORDS!** **PISS ORFF** OR I'LL HAVE YOU **SHOT!!**

DANE'T BE SILLY! YOU DIDN'T BRING YOUR **SHOOTER,** OR AT LEAST I **HAPE** YOU DIDN'T ....

OF COURSE NOT, BUT I CAN STILL **STEB** THE BASTARD WITH ME **COLD STEEL!!**

157

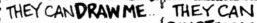

159

161

GORDON OF KHARTOUM

CHRIST I'VE GOT A SORE HEID THIS MORNIN'!

I BRING YOU PARACETAMOL AND A NICE CUP OF TEA, MASTER

©Steve Bell 2007

THANKS CHRIST, YOU'RE A BRICK

GORDON OF KHARTOUM

CHRIST, WHAT IS IT NOW?

EVERY MORNING IT'S THE BLEEDING SAME! YOU WALK DOONSTAIRS AND IT'S THE DEATH OF A THOOSAND CUTS!

THEY WANT YOUR BLOOD, MASTER! NOTHING-PERSONAL, YOU UNDERSTAND

THEN IT'S JUST AS WELL I ONLY HAVE STUFFING

162

GORDON OF KHARTOUM

WHAT IS THIS CREATURE?

It is A **BEAR**

WHAT IS "BEAR"? CULTURALLY I HAVE **NO CONCEPTION** OF "**BEAR**"

IT IS LIKE GOAT **WITHOUT HORNS**

LIKE CAMEL WITHOUT **HUMP**?

5·12·6176·

IN THE WEST **CHILDREN** TAKE THEM TO BED AND **CUDDLE** THEM

WHAT? LIKE PÆDOPHILE NO, LIKE STUFFED **SMALL CAMEL**

I WOULDN'T FANCY CUDDLING **THAT**

©Steve Bell '07

BEARFORCE ONE

—©Steve Bell '07

- 6·12·6177·

BEARFORCE – THERE IS NOWHERE ON **THIS EARTH** WHERE WE CANNOT INTER--VENE TO **END** THE TYRANNY...

...OF **CULTURAL MIS--UNDERSTANDING** AMONG THE SHRIEKING HORDES OF **FUZZY WUZZIES!**

166

January 2008

"For I say unto you, That unto every one which hath shall be given; and from him that hath not, even that he hath shall be taken away from him."

Luke, Chapter 19, verse 26

169

171

WELL DONE, TWAT BOY! J.P. MORGAN, EH?!!

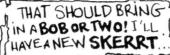

THAT SHOULD BRING IN A **BOB OR TWO**! I'LL HAVE A NEW **SKERRT**...

...AND **YOU** CAN AFFORD TO GET SOME **HURR** TRANSPLANTED FROM YER **CHEST** TO YER **BONCE**!

I ALWAYS THOUGHT YOU WERE A **BIT OF A BANKER**!

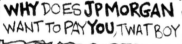

WHY DOES JP MORGAN WANT TO PAY **YOU**, TWAT BOY

THEY WANT MY **STRATEGIC ADVICE**, CHERIE!

YEW COULDN'T STRATEGISE YER WAY OUT OF A **BROWN PAPER BAG**, Y'SILLY **GET**!

I CERTAINLY **COULD** — I'D **SET FIRE** TO IT!

EVEN IF IT WERE **ON** YER 'EAD?

ESPECIALLY IF IT WAS ON MY HEAD!

173

...SO I SAYS TO 'ER: "MY WIFE 'AS POWERS OF WHICH YOU KNOW NUFFINK!

PULL!

"...YOU DON'T 'AVE NO POWER! YOU DON'T EVEN 'AVE NO HRH!!

BLAM

FLING

©Steve Bell '08

SO SHE SAYS: "BUT I CAN DESTROY YOU, BECAUSE I 'AVE THE POWER TO SHAG MUSLIMS!"

THE DIRTY, DIRTY COW!

PULL!

LIZ — THIS POWER OF YOURS... THE ONE OF WHICH WE KNOW NUFFINK?

YEAH, THAT ONE, WHAT'S IT ALL ABAHT?

I TOLD YOU — I KNOW NUFFINK!

©Steve Bell 2008

BUT IF YOU KNOW NUFFINK, 'OW DO YOU KNOW IT'S THERE?

BECAUSE IT'S IN THE BLOOD AN' ONE THING I'M SURE OF...

IF ANY OF US SHAGS A MUSLIM IT ALL GOES AHT THE WINDOW!

PULL!

THAT'S SERIOUS GEL!

175

177

179

AT HOME WITH THE AMERICAN PEOPLE:

WHO COULD THAT BE, HORTENSE?

WHY DON'T YOU GO LOOK SEE?

BING BONG

RAT TAT

© Steve Bell 2008 · 6206·11·2

ARE YOU JOHN Q. FARTBAG?

WHY, YES BUT EVERYONE CALLS ME 'JACK'

WHAT'S THE 'Q' STAND FOR?

QUEEG. I'M RELATED TO MOBY DICK

HOW COME I NEVER KNEW THAT?

THERE'S A LOT YOU DON'T KNOW ABOUT ME, HORTENSE

WHO IS IT ANYWAY?

YEAH - WHO ARE YOU, BUDDY?

I'M THE REPO MAN

6206·12·2

IT'S THE REPO MAN, HONEY! WHAT DOES HE WANT?

I'VE COME TO REPOSSESS YOUR WIFE

2008

Steve Bell

180

183

184

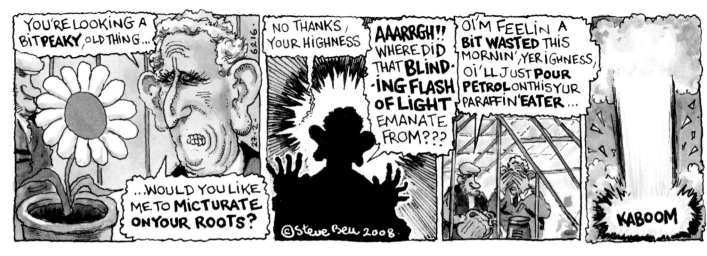

185

March 2008

"The best way to destroy the capitalist system is to debauch the currency. By a continuing process of inflation, governments can confiscate, secretly and unobserved, an important part of the wealth of their citizens."

Lenin

The Old Lady of Threadneedle Street meets Oliver Twist — AFTER GILLRAY — ©Steve Bell 2008- 2659·21·3·

SIX TRILLION BUCKS? THAT'S NOT POSSIBLE!

COURSE IT AIN'T!

THE $3 TRILLION DOLLAR WAR

I MEAN..... THAT'S STOOPID MONEY!

YOU GOT IT!

HOW IN HECK COULD I SPEND A TRILLION IF I DON'T EVEN KNOW WHAT A TRILLION IS?

I REST MY CASE

THREE TRILLION, SIX TRILLION... THIS IS ALL CRAP....

EVEN IF IT WAS THAT MUCH IN THE WAY OF ZEROS IT DON'T MATTER!

6,000,000,000,000

...ON ACCOUNT OF YOU CAN'T PUT A PRICE ON FREEM!

THE COMMANDER-IN-CHIEF DON'T HAVE TO EXPLAIN SQUAT, LET ALONE SPELL IT!

DYE 4 FREEM

188

189

190

2 DAYS TO WAR

WEDNESDAY MARCH 19TH 2003. A COLONEL ADDRESSES HIS TROOPS:

BE PUSILLANIMOUS IN DEFEAT. NEVER ADMIT THAT **ANY GREAT WRONG** CAN **EVER** RESULT FROM OUR INTERVENTION HERE...

TRY AND FORGET THAT WE ARE **NOT WELCOME** AND THAT WE HAVE **NO** MORAL, POLITICAL, SPIRITUAL OR EVEN ECONOMIC JUSTIFICATION FOR OUR PRESENCE IN **THIS ANCIENT LAND**

ABOVE ALL REMEMBER TO IGNORE THE FACT THAT MORE THAN **ONE MILLION PEOPLE** WILL DIE BECAUSE OF THE **POINTLESS CAMPAIGN OF DESTRUCTION** THAT WE SHALL HEREBY INSTIGATE

19.3.6226

1 DAY TO WAR

HEY - BRITISHER **COLONEL DUDE** - I LIKE YOUR **STYLE**!

I'M GONNA HAVE YOUR WISE WORDS **TATTOOED** ON **MY ASS**!

THAT'S A **GREAT HONOUR**, SIR

" **MAGNUM ANUS IN VICTORY** " I LIKE THAT A LOT

HOW DO YOU THINK THAT UP? IT'S SURE CLASSIER THAN "**SHOCK AN' AWE**"!

MAGNUM ANUS IN VICTORY

20.3.6226

©Steve Bell '08

193

THE BiG Picture BOYS

24·3·6228

I SEE **TRUST** SPREADING ACROSS THE MIDDLE EAST, BRINGING **PEACE** IN ITS WAKE, JONATHAN

I ENVISION A TRULY **GLOBAL** AGREEMENT ON CLIMATE CHANGE WITH THE FULL CONFIDENCE OF **ALL THE NATIONS**...

@Steve Bell 2008-

I SEE A PAIR OF **CONTENTED BANKERS** SKIPPING OFF INTO THE SUNSET!

THE BiG PIC-TURE BOYS

JONATHAN... IF I BECOME **PRESIDENT OF EUROPE**...

·25·3·6229·

NOT **IF, WHEN** YOU BECOME PRESIDENT OF EUROPE.

ALRIGHT, **WHEN** I BECOME PRESIDENT OF **EUROPE**, DO YOU THINK...

WE DON'T **THINK**, TONY, WE **MOVE** AND WE **SHAKE**.

@Steve Bell 2008-

194

THE BIG PIC-TURE BOYS

TONY – ARE YOU **HUGGING** YOURSELF AGAIN?

SORRY, JONATHAN, BUT I JUST **CAN'T RESIST MYSELF** AT THE MOMENT...

...NOT ONLY AM I AN MMMM **HAPPY BANKER** BUT, AFTER **FIVE YEARS** OF **UTTER CARNAGE**, THANKS TO YOUR MEMOIRS...

...I'M A **BLESSED PEACEMAKER**! YES! YES!! MMMM!! OOOH! YES! YES! STOP IT JESUS!!!

THE BIG PIC-TURE BOYS

IF THERE ARE **DARK TIMES AHEAD** I KNOW I CAN **WIN THROUGH**...

...BECAUSE I KNOW THAT, **WHATEVER** I MAY OR MAY NOT HAVE **DONE**...

...**JESUS WANTS ME FOR A SUNBEAM**...

...OR, MORE LIKELY, A **FLAMETHROWER**!

195

I KISS 'IM...

I FURNDLE 'IM...

I EVEN LET 'IM PUT 'IS 'EAD UP MA JUPE...

...BUT STILL 'E LOOKS LIKE A FREURGUE

OH DO LOOK! ONE'S PRIME MINISTER SEEMS TO HAVE GORT LORST!

HELLAY MISTER BRINE! DID YOU LOSE YOUR WAY?

I HATE THIS SHITE!

ARE YOU SO FRIGHTFULLY LAIR CLASS YOU DANE'T KNAY WHAT TO WAH?

YOUR FLUNKY TOLD ME TAE WEAR A MAROON DRESS!

MISTER BRINE: A WORD OF ADVICE NEVER LET A FLUNKY TELL YOU WHAT TO WAH!

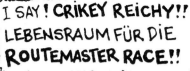

198

200

May 2008

"God has given you one face,
and you make yourself another."

William Shakespeare

THE FIGHTBACK BEGINS TODAY

© Steve Bell 2008-2687 · 23.5.08

GEE UP, DONKEY! WHAT'S THE MATTER WITH THE BEAST?

DONKEY! WAKE UP!! GOOD GOD! LOOK AT ITS EYES!!

THIS DONKEY'S ON CANNABIS!

2008

STRING THE BASTARD UP!!

BUT IT'S NOT STONED IT'S DEAD! YOU'VE FLATTENED IT!

PERHAPS I MAY HAVE BEEN A LITTLE UNFAIR...

...THIS POOR DONKEY NEEDS INCENTIVES TO WORK!

BUT IT'S DEAD!

SO TAKE IT TO PRISON FINE IT ONE POOND AND FIFTY PENCE!

GORDON HOOD GORDON HOOD STRIDING THROUGH THE GLEN...

210

June 2008

"I think George W. Bush has a warm, engaging personality. But, you know, the presidency is more than just a popularity contest."

Al Gore

213

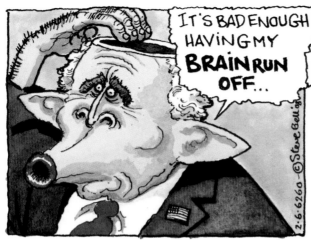

214

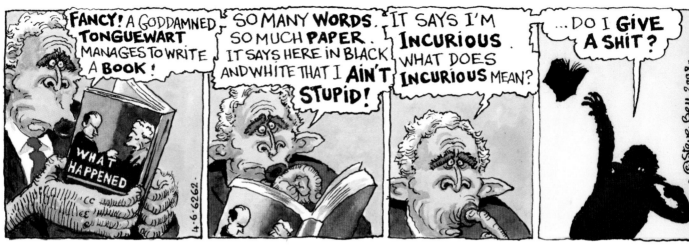

217

THIS CAN'T GO ON...

CHUG BRRMM BOGGLER BOGGLER

16·6·6268·

WE'RE CHOKING OURSELVES TO DEATH!! IT'S TIME TO ACT!

I'M GOING TO BUY A SMART CAR!

LOVE THE PLANET YOU'RE IN

©Steve Bell 2008·

BUY A BIKE, FATTY!!

MAYBE THIS CAR IS A LITTLE TOO SMART

IF YOU'RE SO SMART— TAKE ME TO PECKHAM AND DON'T GIVE ME ANY LIP!

NO!

17·6·6269 - ©Steve Bell 2008·

WHAT DO YOU MEAN NO?! I WANT YOU TO SMELL MY EXHAUST

ALRIGHT— I'M SMELLING YOUR EXHAUST!

AND WHAT IS IT GIVING YOU?

WELL... I'M GETTING TOAST A TOUCH OF VANILLA A HEADY HINT OF PRIVET.... AND THERE'S SOMETHING ELSE...

YES? YES? YES? YES?

...JUST THE MEREST SOUPÇON OF DEAD POLAR BEAR!

HOW DARE YOU!!

218

219

220

MARGARET THATCHER 10

WHERE AM I NOW?

GORDON BROWN!! I AM HE AS YOU ARE SHE...

...AS YOU ARE ME AND WE ARE ALL TOGETHER...

HEEERE'S MAGGIE!

BEGONE FROM THIS PLACE YOU MAD BITCH!!

©Steve Bell '08

MARGARET THATCHER 10

©Steve Bell '08

WHERE AM I NOW?

DON'T TRY AND FIGHT IT, BIG BOY! REMEMBER MY LEGACY!

-26·6·6275- @Steve Bell '08

SAFE IN YOUR HANDS! ONE HOURS SLEEP A NIGHT; THE ONLY FORM OF SOCIAL MOBILITY THAT MATTERS...

...IS KICKING A PAUPER UP THE ARSE! FLY THE FLAG!! DON'T TAKE ANY WOODEN MONEY!...

221

July 2008

"If gay marriage was OK - and I was uncertain on the issue - then I saw no reason in principle why a union should not be consecrated between three men, as well as two men; or indeed three men and a dog."

Boris Johnson

YOUNG MAN, ARE **YOU** GORDON BROWN?

HAIL MARGARET! THE **FREEDOM** OF THIS CITY IS **YOURS!**

THESE **ROUTEMASTER BUSES** ARE YOUR **LOYAL SLAVES,** MARGARET, YOUR **PRAETORIAN GUARD!!**

BUSES?

ARE YOU MAD?

I HATE BUSES MORE THAN I HATE SOCIALISM!!

ABSOLUTELY! COULDN'T AGREE MORE!

WE WHO ARE ABOUT TO DIE **SALUTE YOU!**

OIKS — SHAPE UP OR SHIP OUT!

COME ON YOU TUBBY **COUCH POTATOS!**

YOU'LL NEVER **WIN WIMBLEDON** IF YOU STAY INSIDE WRESTLING WITH YOUR **Wii Wii!**

DON'T LET POLITICALLY INSPIRED **FEAR** OF **PÆDO PERVES** STOP YOU GOING OUT AND **BATTERING BALLS...**

...AND DON'T LET **FEAR OF KNIFE CRIME** PUT YOU OFF EITHER — STABBING SKILLS ARE **FRIGHTFULLY ATHLETIC!**

225

226

CAN I **COUNT ON YOUR VOTE** THIS THURSDAY?

ARE YOU **ANOTHER LOONY?**

NO, I'M STANDING ON A **SERIOUS CIVIL LIBERTIES PLATFORM!**

YES, BUT YOU'RE SHARING A PLATFORM WITH THE **TWENTY FIVE LOONIES!** DOESN'T THAT AFFECT YOUR CAMPAIGN?

© Steve Bell 2008

NOT MATERIALLY, NO...

OKAY DAVIS — YOU'VE **MADE YOUR POINT...**

FORTY TWO DAYS IS A **PILE OF CRAP,** LIBERTY IS UNDER **TERRIBLE THREAT...**

...AND AT THE END OF THE DAY, WHEN ALL'S SAID AND DONE, YOU WILL HAVE ACHIEVED **ONE THING ABOVE ALL ELSE...**

A **MASSIVE SWING TO THE LOONIES!!**

© Steve Bell 2008

PRU-DENCE!

GOR-DON!

PRU-DENCE!!

GOR-DON!

PRU-DENCE!

GOR-DON!

PRU... OOPS!!

POINK

GIVE ME A **STATE FUNERAL**, GOR-DON, OR I SHALL **HAUNT YOU FOREVER!**

BUT YOU'RE **NO DEAD YET**, PRU-DENCE! YOU WILL **NEVER DIE!!**

DEAD, ALIVE — WHO GIVES A **MONKEY'S** AS LONG AS THE **MONEY KEEPS ROLLING IN**, EH?

BWAAAAAAA!

BWAAAHOOOOO!

GOR-DON? WHATEVER IS THE MATTER?

THERE ARE **NO MORE** POONDS, PRU-DENCE!

WE'RE **DOOMED!**

WHAT ABOUT MY **STATE** FUNERAL?

ALL DOOMED!

DON'T DESPAIR GOR-DON! I HAVE A **P.F.I. CONTRACT** HERE...

...SO MY **STATE FUNERAL** WON'T COST YOU A **PENNY**.............YET. JUST SIGN **HERE, HERE, HERE, HERE, HERE, HERE, HERE, HERE, HERE** AND **HERE** ....IN BLOOD.

JUST **IMAGINE** ALL THOSE BRAVE YOUNG MEN MARCHING BEHIND MY **ARMOURED HEARSE** DRAWN BY **EIGHT NAZGUL** WITH **TEN THOUSAND CRUISE MISSILES** SCREAMING OVERHEAD...

...ALL FOR **LESS** THAN THE PRICE OF A **LITRE OF DIESEL** [FOR THE AVOIDANCE OF DOUBT – **YOUR SOUL**].

229

UP THE AMAZON:

WHAT ARE WE DOING HERE?

SHADDAP! WE'RE ON HOLIDAY!

IT DOES MY SOUL GOOD TO GET DOWN AMONG THE TRIBES! AWK!

LOOK WHO'S HERE!!

PRAISE BE! IT'S JASPER YAHYAH AND HIS COAL-FIRED SMART CAR!

HIYA PEEPS!

JASPER!! LOVE YOUR COAL-FIRED SMART CAR!

AAARRGGH! DON'T USE THE 'C' WORD WITH ME!!

YOU MEAN—IT'S NOT COAL-FIRED!

CERTAINLY NOT! THIS SMARTCAR IS POWERED BY THE BENIFICENT EFFUSIONS OF RADIOACTIVE DOG WASTE!

PURR

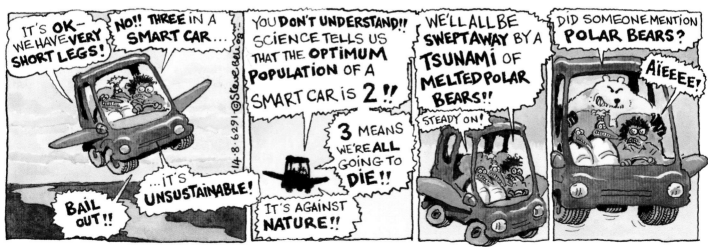

231

...AND SO WE END UP WITH **MILLIONS** OF **SMALL FARMERS** ALL OVER THE WORLD BEING DRIVEN **ORFF THEIR LAND**...

...INTO UNSUSTAINABLE, UNMANAGEABLE, **DEGRADED** AND **DYSFUNCTIONAL CONURBATIONS** OF **UNIMAGINABLE AWFULNESS**...

...LIKE SLOUGH

EH! CONSUELA! LOOK AT THE SIZE OF **MA LIMONS**!

THAS' **WONNERFUL** MANOLITO! YOU KNOW THE MAN FROM THE **DOCHY OF CORNWALL** HE CALL TODAY...

DO HE WAN' **MY LIMONS**?

THE **MAN** FROM THE **DOCHY OF CORNWALL** HE SAY: "**GET ORFF MY LAND!!**"

232

233

September 2008

"What's the difference between a hockey mom and a pit bull? Lipstick."

Sarah Palin

RUNNING MATES

©Steve Bell 2008·2730·5·9·

235

THE GORDY RE-LAUNCHES

15·9·6·2·6·

© Steve Bell 2008

THE GORDY RELAUNCHES

6·2·9·6·

BLAMMO

© Steve Bell 2008

236

THE GORDY RELAUNCHES

TWANNNG

THE GORDY RELAUNCHES

HMS

— THANKS TO ANDY RILEY —

237

THE **GORDY RELAUNCHES**

AND I SAY TO YOU MY FELLOW CONSERVATIVES

...THAT WE MEET HERE, TODAY AT A TIME OF THE GRAVEST IMPORT...

...FOR THE **WORLD**, FOR THE **COUNTRY** FOR THE **BRITISH PEOPLE**...

@Steve Bell 2008

...FOR **OUR PARTY**

FWEEEEP!!

THESE ARE THE DAYS, EH BOZZA?

RATHER!

@Steve Bell 08

BUT HADN'T YOU BETTER **EASE UP** ON THE **SHAMPOO** IN THESE **DIFFICULT TIMES**?

THIS ISN'T '**POO**! THIS IS **SPARKLING ELDERFLOWER**!!

JOLLY **GOOD** SHOW!

NOW — LET'S FIND A **BEGGAR** TO TORMENT!

29.9.6304-

6305·30·9·08

241

244

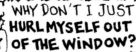

247

November 2008

"It is well enough that people of the nation do not understand our banking and monetary system, for if they did, I believe there would be a revolution before tomorrow morning."

Henry Ford

DON'T LET THE SCRAWNY COMMIE COSMOPOLITAN SPREAD THE WEALTH!

THAT'S SOCIALISM!

WHEN I SPREAD THE OIL WEALTH THAT AIN'T SOCIALISM!!

THAT'S GOOD OL'FASHIONED HONEST-TO-GOODNESS FAMILY-LOVIN' BRIBERY!!

KABOOM

OH BEAUTIFUL FOR SPACIOUS SKIES FOR AMBER WAVES OF GRAIN...

FOR PURPLE MOUNTAIN MAJESTIES ABOVE THE FRUITED PLAIN

AMERICA! AMERICA! GOD SHED HIS GRACE ON THEE...

AND CROWN THY GOOD WITH BROTHERHOOD FROM SEA TO SHINY SEA!!

OH BEAUTIFUL FOR PILGRIM FEET WHOSE STERN IMPASSION'D STRESS

A THOROUGHFARE FOR FREEDOM BEAT ACROSS THE WILDERNESS

AMERICA! AMERICA! GOD MEND THINE EV'RY FLAW

CONFIRM THY SOUL IN SELF-CONTROL THY LIBERTY IN LAW*

* KATHERINE LEE BATES

OH BEAUTIFUL FOR HEROES PROVED IN LIBERATING STRIFE...

WHO MORE THAN SELF THEIR COUNTRY LOVED AND MERCY MORE THAN LIFE...

AFGHANISTAN! AFGHANISTAN! MAY GOD THY GOLD REFINE

TILL ALL SUCCESS BE NOBLENESS AND EV'RY GAIN DIVINE

253

SOCKS IS BACK. ☆ ☆ WHITE HOUSE TRANSITIONAL **CHIEF OF STAFF (FISH)** HERE. HOW MAY I HELP YOU?

IN

OUT

BARRY WANTS YOU TO KNOW THAT HE'S **UP TO SPEED** AND **AHEAD OF THE GAME ON FISH** ALREADY...

...THAT'S WHY HE'S GOT **ME** BACK ON BOARD. **YES,** I AM A GOOD DEAL **OLDER** AND, **YES** I HAVE PUT ON A LITTLE **WEIGHT**...

DO YOU HAVE A **PROBLEM** WITH THAT HAIRBALL?

SOCKS IS BACK AT THE **HUB!** POWER FEELS **GOOOOD!**

FWEEP FWFEP

MOST POWERFUL CAT ON EARTH SPEAKING. HOW MAY I HELP YOU?

DON'T LISTEN TO THE **PUPPY TALK. THE PUPPY** IS **DEAD. PERIOD.**

I KILLED THE PUPPY! SURE. YOU CAN QUOTE ME.

HEY! WHO LET THAT THING IN HERE?

?

I AM NOT A "THING" I AM SOCKS WHITE HOUSE TRANSITIONAL CHIEF OF STAFF (FISH) AND YOU ARE...?

I AM THE PRESIDENT OF THE NICEDAY SMIRKER AND YOU ARE OUTA HERE!

YOU'LL BE HEARING FROM ME, BUDDY!

THE WAR ON TERROR IS OVER...

THE WAR ON FISH STARTS ON JANUARY 20TH

© Steve Bell 2008

WE'RE GONNA GET THE ECONOMY MOVING FROM DAY ONE, AND I'M TELLING YOU THIS...

FAT CATS ARE NOT THE ISSUE; FAT CATS ARE NOT THE PROBLEM; FAT CATS ARE THE ANSWER TO THE PROBLEM!

255

CHARLES, ON **THIS**, THE OCCASION OF YOUR **SIXTIETH BIRTHDAY**, IT GIVES ME GREAT PLEASURE...

... TO PRESENT YOU WITH THIS **UNIQUE CERTIFICATE** IN CELEBRATION

BUT **MA!** THIS IS A TWO-FOR-ONE **KNACKERING SERVICES VOUCHER!**

ROYAL

BOIL-A-NAG

2 FOR 1 OFFER

DEMMIT MA! LOOK AT ME! I'M **RETIRED** BEFORE I'VE EVEN **STARTED** THE BLOODY **JAWB!!**

I'M **TATELY UNEMPLOYABLE** AND IT'S **ALL** YOUR **FAULT!**

NAYBODY UNDERSTANDS ME AT ALL...

... BECAUSE I INHERITED YOUR INCOMPREHENSIBLE **VILE SIGNEDS!!**

GET **IGHT** OF MY **SIGHT!**

LISTEN, BIG YAHS: WHY DON'T YOU STOP BLADDY **MAINING** AND LOOK FOR A **JAWB**?

19.11.6334

GO ON! I **DAH** YOU! HERE IS YOUR **BUS PAWSS**; GET ON YOUR **BUS** AND MAKE YOURSELF **USEFUL**!

BUT MA...

...I DON'T KNOW **HIGH** TO GET ON A BUS. DO I **HAIL IT**, LIKE A TAXICAB? DO I **SNEP MY FINGERS AT IT**, LIKE A **FLUNKEY**?

ALL HAIL, MIGHTY **JUGGERNAUT**!

SNAT SNAT

BOGGLER

WHOOSH

TAKE ME TO **CLARENCE HICE** AND MAKE IT **SNEPPY**!

20.11.6335

BOGGLER BOGGLER

BUS GOES TO **KILBURN**, MATE

BUT I **NEED** TO GO TO **CLARENCE HICE**!

YOU CAN GO TO KILBURN OR YOU CAN **FACK ORFF**, NO OFFENCE

IF WE **DON'T** GO TO CLARENCE HICE...

MY **ARMED RETINUE** WILL BE MOST **PUT IGHT**!

CLARENCE 'ARSE IT IS THEN, MATE!

'OP IN!

257

PRIME MINISTER...

WHAT IS IT, CHANCELLOR?

24·11·6336 ©Steve Bell '08

I WISH TO ISSUE A **PRE-PRE-BUDGET AUTUMN STATEMENT STATEMENT**

HOW VERY LAUDABLE AND **FAR-SIGHTED** OF YOU CHANCELLOR

WE'RE ALL **FUCKED** AND I'M **RUNNIN'** OOT O' **MOGADON!**

STEADY ON THERE, CHANCELLOR

TEAR

TEAR TEAR

NNNGHNYEEE!! NNYEEEE!

STOP IT CHANCELLOR! YOU'LL **DAMAGE** YOURSELF!

WRENCH RIP

©Steve Bell 2008

25·11·6337

I DON'T **CARE!** I'M GAUNTAE **RIP OOT** MA **EYEBROOS!!**

WHY DESTROY YOUR **CROWNING GLORY**, CHANCELLOR?

NNGHHNYEEE! NNGGNNYEE!!

RIP

WHY NOT? THERE'S **BUGGER ALL** ELSE I CAN DO ABOOT ANYTHING!

PERHAPS YOU HAVE A POINT, CHANCELLOR

258

DO YOU **FEEL BETTER** NOW, CHANCELLOR?

I FEEL LIKE A MAN WITH **NAE EYEBROOS**

THEY'LL **NEVER GROW BACK**, Y'KNOW

YOU'RE FAR TOO **PESSIMISTIC**, MAN! JUST LEAVE IT 12 MONTHS, THEN STICK YER **HEID** IN THIS **BARREL OF MONEY**.

BUGGER THAT! I'M NO WAITIN' **12 MONTHS** TO REGROW MA **EYEBROOS!**

STEADY CHANCELLOR!

I'M **PLUNGIN'** MA **HEID** IN YON BARREL O' MONEY **RIGHT NOO!**

PRIME MINISTER! THE **MONEY** IN THIS BARREL IS MADE OF **WOOD!**

I'M AFRAID THE SITUATION IS **WORSE THAN WE THOUGHT** CHANCELLOR

I'M FRANKLY **DISAPPOINTED**, PRIME MINISTER

HERE ARE TWO MOGADON AND SOME **GLUE** FOR YOUR EYEBROOS, CHANCELLOR

259

'TWAS THE **NIGHT** BEFORE CHRISTMAS...

...AND ALL ROUND THE HOUSE...

...NOT A CREATURE WAS STIRRING...

...EXCEPT THE **MINISTER FOR WORK AND PENSIONS**

THE **RODENT** HE SAT BY THE CHIMNEY WITH CARE

...IN HOPE THAT **ST NICHOLAS** SOON WOULD BE THERE

...HE WAS PLANNING TO **SEIZE THE OLD ELF** BY THE EAR

...FOR THE SCHEMING OLD SOD WORKED BUT **ONE DAY A YEAR**

260

AND THEN ALL AT ONCE CAME A LOUD FARTING SOUND...

17.12.63.42

PHHRRRP

...DOWN THE CHIMNEY SAINT NICHOLAS CAME WITH A BOUND..

©Steve Bell 2008

...HE SHOWED NOT A BLUSH, THAT SHAMELESS OLD RUIN...

YOU'RE NICKED, NICK!

...SAID:"I HAPPENED TO PASS, SAW YOUR ROOF NEEDED DOIN'"

?

YOUR ROOF'S IN GOOD HANDS YOU CAN LEAVE IT TO ME FOR THREE HUNDRED QUID AND A NICE CUP OF TEA...

8.12. 63.42

...COME LOUNGER COME SCROUNGER COME SHIRKER AND WASTER COME LESBIAN LIL AND HER OLD TURKEY BASTER

...TO THE TOP OF THE ROOF TO THE TOP OF THE WALL NOW CLAIM AWAY! CLAIM AWAY! CLAIM AWAY ALL!!

©Steve Bell '08

261

AWAY FROM THE ROOFTOP, THE CLAIMANTS THEY FLEW... ..WITH A SLEIGH FULL OF GIROS, SAINT NICHOLAS TOO...

WHO'D SIT AT THE POLE IN HIS FUR-TRIMMED RED RAYMENT... QUITE SNUG ALL YEAR LONG CLAIMING COLD WEATHER PAYMENT

TASTY SNACKS

THE RAT WAS ENRAGED AND LEAPT UP AT THE SLEIGH.. "I'LL HAVE YOU IN JAIL BY THIS CHRISTMAS DAY!" "YOU BREED AND YOU SPONGE LIKE A FESTERING CANKER.. ..TAKING BREAD FROM THE MOUTHS OF EACH POOR NEEDY BANKER!"

© Steve Bell 2008 · 23·12·6315

"WEALTH CREATORS NEED PERKS SCROUNGING SCUM NEED A BEATING...

24·12·63646

...SO GET OUT TO WORK! IF IT WON'T PAY, STOP EATING!"

CHOMP

BUT SANTA SAID: "BOLLOCKS TO THAT, RATTY SNOOPER! I THINK YOU SHOULD MEANS TEST THIS KICK UP THE POOPER!"

...AND HE CALLED TO THE RAT AS HE FLEW OUT OF SIGHT: "UNIVERSAL BENEFITS TO ALL, AND NEW LABOUR GOOD NIGHT!"

263

January 2009

"I'm telling you there's an enemy
that would like to attack America,
Americans, again. There just is.
 That's the reality of the world.
And I wish him all the very best."

George W. Bush, 12 January 2009

ONLY FIVE MORE BOMBING DAYS TO BUSHLESS

©Steve Bell 2009-15·1·2783

266

AT LAST! MY DREAM HAS COME TRUE!

MY VERY OWN TOXIC BANK!

COME!!

YES?

I'D LIKE TO DEPOSIT SOME UNMENTIONABLES

WHY THANKYOU! HAVE THIS BUNCH OF ROSES!!

RUPT BANK

26·1·63   ©Steve Bell 2009–

RED ROSES!? FOR ME? WHY THANKYOU!!

NOW, ABOUT THESE UN-MENTIONABLES YOU WISH TO DEPOSIT....

YOU WISH TO EXCHANGE THEM FOR HARD CURRENCY?

©Steve Bell '09

27·1·6352

I DO INDEED! I'M OFFERING YOU A GUARANTEED SUPPLY OF EXCEPTIONAL QUALITY UNSPEAKABLE FILTH!!

I CAN GIVE YOU THIS DEAD DOG... ...OR WOULD YOU PREFER A CHEQUE?

ER... CAN I HAVE A **CHEQUE**?

OF COURSE! ACTUAL **DEAD DOGS** CAN BE CONSIDERED **OFFENSIVE** IN SOME CULTURES

"I PROMISE TO PAY THE BEARER THE SUM OF **FIVE HUNDRED THOUSAND DEAD DOGS**" IS SO MUCH MORE **CONVENIENT**...

...AND **LOOK**: THE DEAD DOG IS **RISING STEADILY** AGAINST ALL CURRENCIES

THAT'S WHY **BARCLAYS** HAS PICKED UP LATELY! **THINK ABOUT IT**

THIS IS **MARVELLOUS**! I'M PUTTING **EVERY-THING** INTO **DEAD DOGS**!

IF YOU DON'T MIND ME SAYING:— THAT'S THE **SHREWDEST MOVE** YOU'LL EVER MAKE! ONE WORD OF **ADVICE**, THOUGH...

AVOID DEAD DOG FUTURES IF POSSIBLE...

...AND AT ALL COSTS STEER CLEAR OF **DEAD DOG FUTURES DERIVATIVES**!

©Steve Bell 2009

THAT PRAYER BREAKFAST, IN FULL....

TAKE AWAY THE FLESH OF THE SWINE!

BRING ME CHEERIOS!

IN THE NAME OF THE BURGER, THE BUN AND THE WHOLEMEAL TOAST...

DON'T HAVE A COW MO!

MY GOOD FRIEND TONY BLAIR - MAY YOU GO FORTH AND MULTIPLY...

MAY I BASK IN THE WARM GLOW OF YOUR SINCERITY!

OMMMM MMMMM MMMM...

I AM THE GOD OF HELLFIRE AND I BRING YOU....

FI-YAH!! DOO DOO DOOOO... CHEESE N CRACKERS GOT ALL MUDDY....

~ AFTER LEONARDO + ARTHUR BROWN ~

TONY BLAIR, MY VERY GOOD FRIEND - HOW'S IT HANGIN'?

WELL, RADIANCE, MY REPUTATION WAS HANGING BY A THREAD UNTIL YOU WELCOMED ME INTO YOUR CHARMED CIRCLE!

MY CASSOCK, ON THE OTHER HAND, HAS NEVER HUNG BETTER!

HMMM

I'M SO FULL OF FAITH I COULD FLY LIKE A FISH!!

272

SAY! HOW DO YOU DO THAT THING??

WHAT, **THIS** OLD THING WITH **MY EARS**?

THAT IS SOME **SERIOUS SHIT**, MY FRIEND!

I DO IT WHEN I'M **ALL FAITHED UP**, RADIANCE. I CAN **MOVE MOUNTAINS**, I CAN **BRING PEACE** TO THE **MIDDLE EAST**..

...AND I CAN **FLY LIKE A FISH**! HERE — **YOU** TRY IT! YOU HAVE ALL THE **RIGHT EQUIPMENT**

IT'S **NOT WORKING**, TONY MY GOOD FRIEND! **WHY** CAN'T I **FLY LIKE A FISH**?

HMMMM

YOU HAVE THE **EARS**, YOU HAVE THE **TEETH** ...BUT DO YOU HAVE **THE FAITH**??

SURE I HAVE! I'M PRAYIN' AS HARD AS I CAN GODDAMMIT!!

I'M SORRY, GILDED ONE, BUT YOU JUST MAY NOT HAVE **THE EYEBALLS**!

276

277

March 2009

"But down the pit… you know full well that she can be a nasty bitch when she likes … And if you're not sharp enough and don't get out of the way of her, she'll kill you."

Miner quoted in *The Big Hewer*, BBC Radio Ballad, 1961

STILLWORKING OVERTIME:

JUSTICE FOR MINEWORKERS

TRUTH &

RECONCILIATION

COMMISSION

279

ONLY LAST WEEK:

PORTUGUESE WATER HOUND?!?

DON'T GIVE THAT 'PORTUGUESE WATER HOUND' CRUUURRGHH!

CRUNCH...!

SOCKS R.I.P.

EVEN EARLIER LAST WEEK:

THIS IS STANDARD VETTING PROCEDURE, MR....ER...

RAO!

SO, MR RAO, HOW LONG HAVE YOU BEEN A PORTUGUESE WATER HOUND?

RAO!

RAO!

ARE YOU OR HAVE YOU EVER BEEN INVOLVED IN A CAMPAIGN OF ANTI-FELINE GENOCIDAL MURDER?

RAO! RAO!!

RAO! RAO!! RAO!!!

280

281

282

'ELLO MUM   PERCY!

WHERE HAVE YOU BEEN THIS LAST FIFTEEN YEARS?   AROUND

©Steve Bell 2009

WHAT HAVE YOU BEEN DOING ALL THIS TIME?   STUFF...

...SKUNK MAINLY

PERCY!   YES, MUM?

ARE YOU IN A RELATION-SHIP WITH THAT SKUNK?   MUM! PLEASE!!

I MEAN...ARE YOU IN A PHYSICALLY ADDICTIVE RELATIONSHIP?   F*** OFF MUM!

YOU WON'T MIND IF I VIDEO EVERY-THING YOU DO AND SAY....

I REMEMBER THE SEVENTIES WHEN EVERYTHING WAS **BRAHN!**

ME **MUVVER** SMOKED, ME **FARVER** SMOKED, ME **BABY BRUVVER** SMOKED, AND JUST BECAUSE YOU WORE A **MOUSTACHE**...

...DIDN'T MEAN YOU WAS A **POOF.** EVERYBODY WAS **ON THE TAKE,** INCLUDING THE VICAR...

...**TRADE UNION BULLY BOYS** RULED THE ROOST, AND ALL WOMEN WERE **SLAGS** EXCEPT FOR THE **QUEEN** AND **MRS THATCHER**

I REMEMBER THE **SEVENTIES** WHEN EVERYBODY WAS **ON STRIKE**...

ME **MUVVER** WAS ON **STRIKE,** ME **FARVER** WAS ON STRIKE, ME **BABY BRUVVER** WAS ON STRIKE. ME **BARBER** WAS ON STRIKE, WHICH MEANT...

...I WAS STARTIN' TO **LOOK LIKE A POOF.** EVEN THE VICAR WAS ON STRIKE...

WE 'AD BEEN PAYIN' OURSELVES **TOO MUCH** FOR PRODUCIN' **TOO LITTLE** FOR **TOO LONG.** THE COUNTRY NEEDED A **KICK UP THE ARSE,** SO I JOINED THE **FILTH!**

287

288

ATTENTION! HERE COMES THE **GREAT ARCHITECT**! THE MAN WITH THE **MIDAS TOUCH**!

ARE YOU FEELING ALRIGHT, PIUS?

© Steve Bell 2009

GORDON BROWN! FRESH FROM HIS **TRIUMPH** AT THE **G20 SUMMIT**! THE MAN WHO SHOWED THE WORLD THE **WAY FORWARD**! EVERYTHING HE **TOUCHES** TURNS TO...

BOLLOCKS! WHY DOES **EVERYTHING** I TOUCH TURN TO **BOLLOCKS**?

MAKE WAY FOR THE **GRAND TESTICULATOR**! THE MAN WITH THE **SCROTAS TOUCH**!

HELLO BIRDS!

© Steve Bell 2009

HELLO FLOWERS!

HELLO ALASTAIR!

GET AWAY FROM ME YOU FREAK!

YOU'RE AWFULLY **BIG** FOR A WARBLER

THAT'S **ENOUGH SIZE-IST** REMARKS. I AM THE **FUTURE OF WARBLING**, AND WHAT'S MORE...

...I WANT **MORE SNACKS** AND I WANT THEM **NOW!**

THINK OF ME AS YOUR **PENSION FUND!!**

CRIKEY!

WHAT HAPPENED TO THE **FUTURE OF WARBLING**?

HE MUST HAVE GONE TO **SWITZERLAND!**

BRRAAARRRP!

WE CLEARLY WEREN'T FEEDING HIM **ENOUGH!**

291

May 2009

"Beware of little expenses.
A small leak will sink
a great ship."

Benjamin Franklin

Benefit thieves
We're closing in

295

GORDON! I'M YOUR REPLACEMENT SPIN SUPREMO!

LET'S BE POSITIVE - THERE'S NEVER BEEN A BETTER TIME TO PUT ON A PIG MASK...

...AND GO 'AAACHOO!!'

TADAA! BOOM! BOOM!

EXCELLENT IDEA! WHAT DO I DO NEXT?

I'M SO TIRED... I'LL JUST TAKE A NAP IN THIS CONVENIENT GUTTER

GORDON - WHAT A GREAT IDEA!

AND LOOK: IT'S PAYING OFF! ALREADY YOU'VE GOT A NEW FRIEND...

YOUTUBE IF YOU WANT TO...OINK!

I'M NOT CORROOPT! MY BROTHER DRIVES A BOOS!

...AND SHE'S A VOTER MAGNET!

296

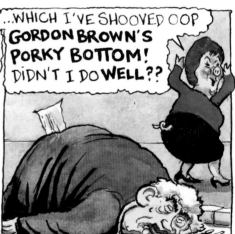

DWP
Department for
Work and Pensions

TARGETING

BENEFIT THEFT

©SteveBell 18·5·6403—

THANKS TO RICHARD NEWSON—

10

We're closing in

Ugly, low class people...

19·5·6404 ©SteveBell'09

We're closing in

Royalty...

SOUTH PORK SOLD

we're backing off

299

302

DAVE THE JELLYFISH

NOW DAVE — ANSWER ME THIS QUESTION:

HAVE YOU EVER TAKEN A BUNG FROM ANYONE?

EMPHATICALLY NO! I WOULD NEVER TAKE ANY FORM OF BRIBE!

I HAVE A CHAP WHO LOOKS AFTER THAT SORT OF THING

-3·6·6413-

©Steve Bell 2009

HI! I'M DAVE THE JELLYFISH!

MY FAMILY OWNS HALF OF BERKSHIRE

MY WIFE'S FAMILY OWNS HALF OF LINCOLNSHIRE

THAT'S WHY I NEEDED PUBLIC HELP TO BUY A SPECIAL JELLYFISH HOME

...OTHERWISE I'D BE NOTHING MORE THAN A WASHED UP BLOB OF SNOT

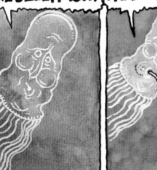

-4·6·6414-

©Steve Bell 2009.

303

© Steve Bell 2009 – after Ingmar Bergman –

8·6·6415

SNAP!

BUGGER!

I THOUGHT WE WERE PLAYING **CHESS**

ALL RIGHT! YOU CAN HAVE **MY** TROOSERS!

© Steve Bell 2009 · 9·6·6416·

FULL HOUSE!

OCH **SHITE!**

I HAVEN'T A STITCH LEFT

THAT'S **NOT** A PROBLEM!

BESET BY **DEMONS**, STARK NAKED IN THE **BOWELS OF HELL**, THE **FIGHTBACK** STARTS **HERE!**

BRITISH JOBS FOR BRITISH WORKERS

I'M **BACK** FROM THE **HOBS** OF HELL...

...AND I'VE JUST GOT **ONE THING** TO SAY BEFORE WE GET **BACK TO BUSINESS**:

LORD SHIT — YOU'RE HIRED!

LORD SHIT — YOU'RE **ENTERPRISE TSAR.** GIVE ME YOUR **INPUT!**

THE NAME'S **SUGAR!**

YOU'VE CHANGED YOUR NAME! WHAT A **BRILLIANT STRATEGY!** FROM NOW ON I'LL BE **GORDON PINK!**

I DO BEG YOUR PARDON, LORD SUGAR — I SEEM TO HAVE MADE AN **ELEMENTARY** ERROR...

YOU'RE TIRED!

THE MOTHER OF PARLIAMENTS

BY THE RIGHT QUICK MARCH! RUMPTY TUMP RUMPTY TUMP RUMPETY TUMP

I AM ONE OF THE EX-MILITARY TYPES THAT RUNS THIS 'OUSE...

...AND I'M TELLIN' YOU TO PUT SOME TRIZERS ON! SHOW SOME RESPECT! THIS IS NO ORDINARY WEEK!

BUT...BUT... I'M A BISHOP!

THIS IS POMPOUS HAS-BEEN OF THE DECADE AWARD WEEK! GET YOUR 'AIR CUT!

BUT...BUT... I'M A WOMAN!

PUT THAT LIGHT OUT!

POMPOUS HAS BEEN? CHAIR FILLER? LOTS OF BOTTOM? YOUR HOUSE NEEDS YOU

NAME? ARE YOU A POMPOUS HAS-BEEN?

MAD FRANKIE FIELD

I AM

CAN YOU FILL A CHAIR WITH BOTTOM?

I CAN

RIGHT, YOU'RE ON THE LIST! NEXT!! NAME?

ANN SQUEAKY WIDDECOMBE

AREN'T YOU A BIT SHORT?

YES, COULD YOU LOAN ME HALF A CROWN?

309

July 2009

"Under the various Geneva Conventions and protocols, all prisoners, however they are described, are entitled to the same levels of protection. You have commented on their treatment. It appears from your description that they may not be being treated in accordance with the appropriate standards. Given that they are not within our custody or control, the law does not require you to intervene to prevent this."

HM Government advice to its intelligence and security officers, quoted in the *Guardian*, July 2010

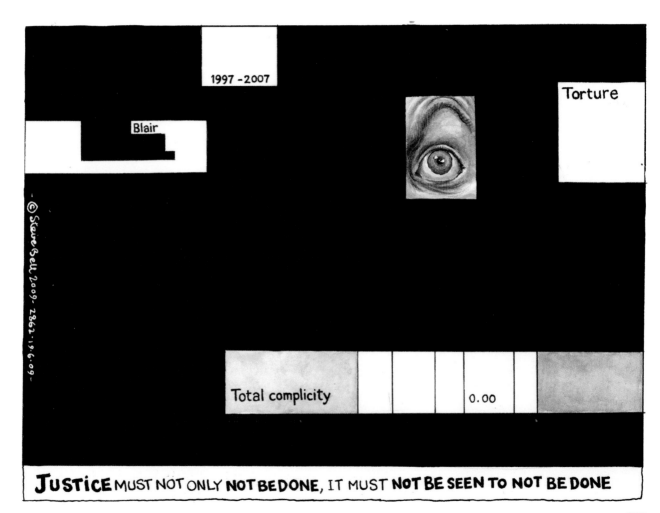

1997 - 2007

Torture

Blair

© Steve Bell 2009 - 2862 · 19·6·09 -

Total complicity   0.00

JUSTICE MUST NOT ONLY **NOT BE DONE**, IT MUST **NOT BE SEEN TO NOT BE DONE**

TERRIBLE BUSINESS, THIS PHONE HACKING, RUPE..

-13·7·6435-

DID **YOU** KNOW IT WAS ILLEGAL? **NEITHER DID I!**

DO WE NEED TO **REOPEN** THE INVESTIGATION? HANG ON – **I'LL CHECK...**

©Steve Bell '09

CLANK

WE SEE NO NEED TO RE-OPEN THE INVESTIGATION

I REPEAT: WE SEE **NO NEED** TO RE-OPEN THE INVESTIGATION. I'M SORRY, COULD YOU **REPEAT THAT, RUPE?** THIS SIGNAL'S A BIT....

14·7·6436

...**THAT'S BETTER!**

YOU WANT TO SEND ME A **BUNCH OF FLOWERS** AND A COUPLE OF **DRINKS?**

NOW YOU KNOW THAT **WOULD** BE **COMPLETELY ILLEGAL**, RUPE, SO I'LL SEND MY MONKEY ROUND TO EXPLAIN THE **NICETIES**

©Steve Bell 2009-

317

HUP! HUP! HUP!

·20·7·6439·

HUG A HOODIE!

THEN NICK HIS PHONE!

AND WE NEED MORE JELLYCOPTERS!

·©Steve Bell 2009·

HOODIE ON A BIKE — STOP RIGHT THERE!

21·7·6440·

HUG HIM, NICK HIS PHONE...

NICK HIS BIKE...

© Steve Bell 2009

GIVE HIM A TWENTY FIRST CENTURY CLIP ROUND THE EAR WITH A JELLYCOPTER!!

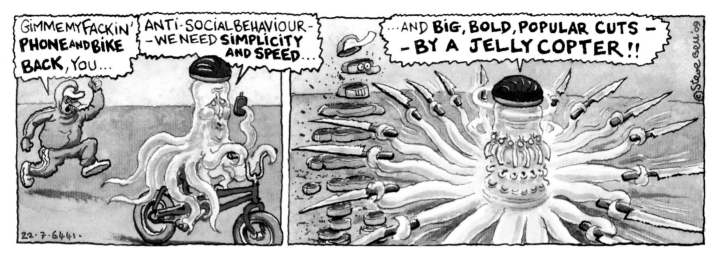

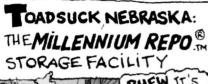

320

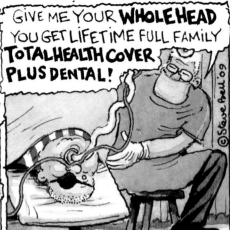

September 2009

"The proprietor may have changed his mind, but I don't think the readers want the sun to set on New Labour."

Lord Mandelson

326

328

329

330

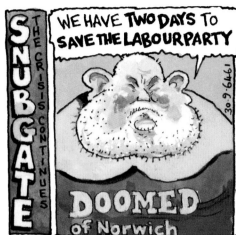

334

335

THE PRIME MINISTER'S PROBLEM IS **PERFECTLY CLEAR**, OR RATHER, **UNCLEAR**.

HE IS QUITE SIMPLY **NOT TRANSPARENT ENOUGH!**

THAT IS SIMPLY **NOT THE CASE**, AS I SHALL DEMONSTRATE...

...BY BRINGING IN **COMPULSORY NAKED STRANGER X-RAY MACHINES** FOR **ALL** MEMBERS OF PARLIAMENT!

THE DEBATE HOTS UP:

SO, **BUMFACE**, WHAT HAVE **YOU** GOT TO HIDE?

NAKED STRANGER X-RAY · LIVE BODY IMAGING

ABSOLUTELY **NOTHING**, OF COURSE, BUT WHAT'S **THAT**?

NAKED STRANGER X-RAY LIVE BODY IMAGING

THAT'S WHERE MY **BROTHER** LEFT HIS **TROWEL** — AND IT'S UTTERLY **SPOTLESS!**

NAKED STRANGER X-RAY LIVE BODY IMAGING

COME ON, P.L.P!...

TM NAKED STRANGER BODY IMAGING

·21·10·6473·

...YOU **LABOUR MPs** MUST DO YOUR BIT FOR **OPEN GOVERNMENT** BY SUBMITTING YOURSELVES TO ᵀᴹ **NAKED STRANGER**® BODY IMAGING!

IF YOU'VE **NOTHING TO HIDE** YOU'VE NOTHING TO **WORRY ABOUT!**

COME ON, YOU **WINDY SCUM!** - WE'RE STARING **VICTORY** IN THE FACE HERE!!

NAKED STRANGER

I SPY **NAKED STRANGERS!**

THE LEADER OF THE OPPOSITION IS UNWILLING TO SUBMIT TO **LIVE BODY IMAGING!**

NAKED STRANGER

22·10·6474·

...HE IS THEREFORE A **POSSIBLE TERRORIST!**

THAT IS AN **OUTRAGEOUS SLUR!**

SO, **WHAT** HAS HE GOT TO **HIDE?**

...TRANGER

NOTHING WHATEVER. THAT IS MY CENTRAL **PROBLEM.**

NAKED STRANGER

339

November 2009

"I've got a large bucket of shit lying on my desk and tomorrow morning I'm going to pour it all over your head."

Kelvin MacKenzie, then editor of the Sun to John Major, then Prime Minister

THE Sun

Respect Our Cannon Fodder

You Shameful Blundering Scotch Bastard

LISTEN, COWFACE: THERE ARE MANY REASONS FOR MY **SUPERIOR PLAUSIBILITY** AS A **LIFE FORM**...

I AM **RARER** THAN YOU TWO-A-PENNY GRASS-GUZZLING **FARTBOXES**!!

...I HAVE **POWERFUL JAWS** WHICH I'M QUITE PREPARED TO USE, AND, **THIS** IS THE **CLINCHER**:

I DON'T FART!

YOU MEAN – YOU SMELL LIKE THAT ALL THE TIME?

© Steve Bell '09

YOU'RE JUST AN **INDUSTRIAL UNIT** FUELLING THE **HUMAN VERMIN**!

5-11-6482-

I AM A **FIFTY SEVEN STONE** FRIEND OF **FREEDOM**!

– © Steve Bell 2009 –

I **SEEK SEALS** AND **FIGHT FLATULENCE**...

...AND I DON'T SMELL!

IGNORE THE FAT FASCIST! **KEEP FARTING THROUGH**!

344

345

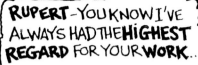

347

348

I LIKE **CHEESE** UND I LIKE ♫ **ŒUF**...

25·11·64½·93

I'M AN **EVIL** LITTLE SMŒUF! ♫

I'M BRIGHT BLUE UND HERE'S **DER ROOB**... ♫

©Steve Bew·09

...**EUROPE** IS A **CHRISTIAN CLOOB!**

I HAVE GOT A ♫ **GREAT BIG JOB**....

26·11·64½·94
©Steve Bell·2009·

...AND I HAVE A **BRIGHT BLUE KNOB** ♫...

...MY BIG JOB HAS **LOTS OF PERKS**...♫

...AND IT'S **PISSIN'** OFF DE **TURKS!** ♫ ♪

349

352

353

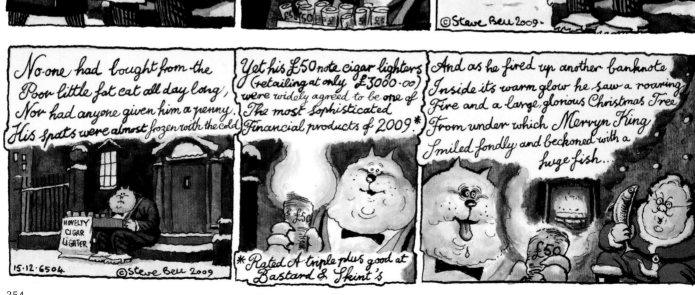

The note fizzled out and the little Fat cat was colder than ever. He looked up at the sky above the banks And saw a star falling. He thought:

SOMEONE IS GOING OFFSHORE!

For the cat's old mistress, Mad Mag, the only one who had Ever tickled him, had told him That whenever a star falls a banker Was going offshore. The cat made Haste to fire up all the £50 notes.

And they glowed with light brighter Than the noon-day and Mad Mag Appeared, larger and more Glorious than a christmas tree

"O take me with you Mad Mag!" cried the fat little cat, "For I know You will vanish when the £50 notes burn out!" And he made haste to set fire to his spats and shirt.

And Mad Mag took the Fat little cat by the scruff of The neck and they both flew Upwards in brightness and joy.

Far above the earth, where there was Neither cold nor hunger nor pain, For they were with God, offshore.

APOLOGIES TO HANS CHRISTIAN ANDERSEN

355

January 2010

"You wouldn't airbrush a photo of yourself, would you?"
"I certainly hope not!"

David Cameron, interviewed on BBC R4's *Today*, 7 January 2010

357

THE NAME'S **HOON**,

JAMES HOON AGENT OF **BRITISH INTELLIGENCE**,

I CAN DO A **GUARDIAN** CROSSWORD IN **SIX SECONDS FLAT**, I AM LICENCED TO **KILL BROWN**,

I USED TO HAVE **A MOUSTACHE!**

— Steve Bell 2010 —

THE NAME'S **PIT** **PITRICIA HEWITT**

IT'S TIME TO **CLEAR THE EAR** AND **STOP** ALL THE **NIGATIVE BRIEFING**

I BELIEVE THAT **GORDON** NEEDS TO **LOSE HIS JOB**,

BECAUSE **THET** WOULD BE THE **SINGLE BIST THING** FOR THE FUTURE OF THE BRITISH **PRIVATE HILTHCUR** INDUSTRY SINCE **ME!**

©Steve Bell 2010

361

45 MINUTES TO CURTAIN UP MR DE BLAIR!

ZZZ ZZZ ZZZ

25·1·6515·

THE DAGGER AND THE SKULL ARE ON THE CHAIR BEHIND YOU

YES, YES

ALAS POOR PRESCOTT, I KNEW HIM WELL...

©Steve Bell 2010

TO BUGGER BROWN OR NOT TO BUGGER BROWN? WHAT A STUPID QUESTION!

NNNGHH! RRRRRR!! RRR! RRRRR!!

STOP YER WRIGGLIN' TWAT BOY!

26·1·6516·

YET HERE'S A SPOT!

OUT DAMNED SPOT! OUT I SAY!

HERE'S THE SMELL OF BLOOD STILL! ALL THE PERFUMES OF ARABIA WILL NOT SWEETEN THIS LITTLE HAND! OH! OH! OH!!

SO IT'S JUST AS WELL I'M HAPPY CLAPPY CLAPPY HAPPY HA..AWWK!!

THOK

©Steve Bell 2010·

FOR **CENTURIES** PEOPLE HAVE SEARCHED FOR SOMETHING THAT IS **BELOW A TANK TOP**...

...BUT **MORE THAN A BARE BOTTOM**. WE THINK WE'VE FOUND A **NEAT SOLUTION**...

...AND WE CALL IT THE **iPANT** !

IT **GLOWS IN THE DARK**, AND IT COSTS AN **ARM AND A LEG**. IT'S LIKE A **HOLY GRAIL FULL OF NUCLEAR WASTE** !!

ONLY $4.99

...BUT THE SINGLE **GREATEST THING** ABOUT THE **iPANT** IS THIS :

HI!

YOU CAN PUT IT ON **OVER YOUR HEAD** LIKE SO...

YOU'RE $499 POORER   NOW GET THE

...AND SUDDENLY ACHIEVE A **360°** PANORAMA EFFECT

CRAP APP

IT'S **EXACTLY** LIKE **REAL LIFE**, BUT YOU CAN **CHOOSE** WHEN AND WHERE YOU CAN **FRY YOUR OWN HEAD**! NOW I'M HERE!   NOW I'M **NOT**!

ONLY $49

...DID I SAY **SINGLE** GREATEST THING? WHAT **CAN I** HAVE BEEN THINKING OF?

THE **iPANT** HAS SO MANY **GREAT FEATURES**: YOU CAN **TALK** TO YOUR **FRIENDS** THROUGH IT, LIKE A KIND OF MAGIC **BUILDER'S PLANK!**

BUT WHAT BEATS ALL IS THAT YOU **DIAL UP** AND **BUY** EVERY BOOK IN THE **WORLD** SIMULTANEOUSLY!

I AM **NOW** ONE OF THE **GREAT LIBRARIES** OF HUMAN CIVILIS...

BUGGER!

-3-2-6521-

iSMASH   iTiNKLE

©Steve Bell 2010

I'M **VERY GLAD** THAT HAPPENED, BECAUSE **BROKEN iPANT NIGHTMARE SYNDROME** IS SOMETHING **NO-ONE** SHOULD HAVE TO FEAR...

...AND OUR UNIQUE **iPANT PROTECTION PACKAGE** CAN BRING YOU **PEACE OF MIND...**

FOREVER!

AND ALL IT COSTS IS **ONE ARM** AND **ONE LEG PER MONTH!**

-4-2-6521-

©Steve Bell 2010

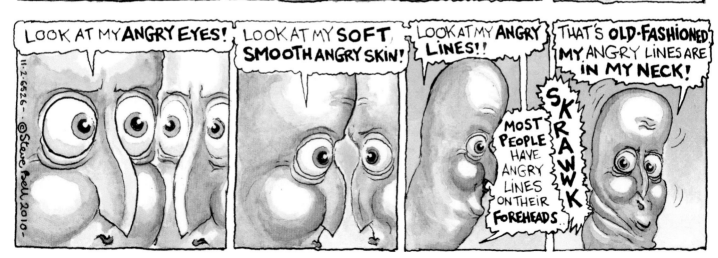

368

369

March 2010

"The forces of hell were unleashed."

Alistair Darling, Sky News February 23rd 2010

- © Steve Bell 2010 - AFTER GUSTAVE DORÉ - 2973·25·2·10·

371

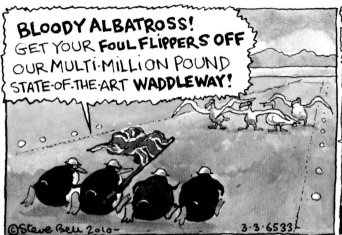

I WOULD **NEVER EVER** ...

...HAVE **WITHHELD** OR BEEN IN ANY WAY **PARSIMONIOUS** WITH **POONDS** FOR THE **POOR** ...

... **I DO BEG YOUR PARDON**, I SHOULD HAVE SAID: "**POONDS FOR THE WAR**"

THE **IRAQ INQUIRY**

TONY, MY MAN! YOU'RE LOOKIN' **SLEEKIT!**

HOW'S IT **HANGIN'** THE **NOO?**

TONY BLAIR THE JOURNEY

THIS **JOURNEY** YOU TALK ABOUT IN YOUR BOOK — **WHERE** IS IT YOU'RE **OFF TO?**

IT'S, HEY, LOOK, Y'KNOW, KINDA **METAPHORICAL** ...

IT'S ABOUT FINDING A **TRUE PATH** ...

...TO THE **NEAREST BANK!** I LIKE YOUR **THINKING!**

THE JOURNEY IS A SPIRITUAL THING, GORDON, WHICH OF COURSE YOU WOULDN'T UNDERSTAND...

...BECAUSE YOU HAVE ALL THE SPIRITUAL SENSITIVITY OF A LARGE TURD!

THE JOURNEY IS ABOUT A QUEST, A SEARCH FOR A SPIRITUAL HOME, AN ATTEMPT TO FIND...

SOMEWHERE BEYOND THE REACH OF THE INTERNATIONAL CRIMINAL COURT

I'M WITH YOU ALL THE WAY, TONY!

DON'T PISS ME OFF, GORDON!

...OR I WON'T ENDORSE YOU IN THE GENERAL ELECTION CAMPAIGN. YOU NEED ME, GORDON!

GRRWRRR RRRRRRRR GGGGGRRR MNNNINNN

WORCESTER WOMAN NEEDS ME TO GET HER BACK IN LABOUR!

FUGGNNN WUGGGRR WMMMNN GRRRRR!

NOT TO MENTION LIVERPOOL LADY!!

I LUV YEW, GORDON! I'LL BE THURR FOR YEW... ...MATE!

376

378

379

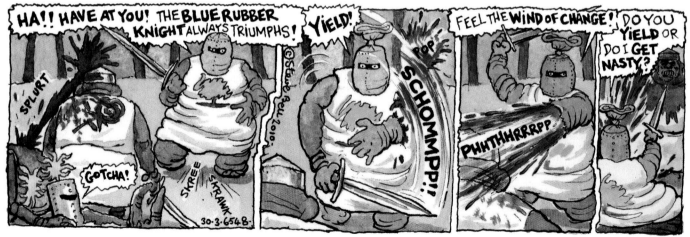

381

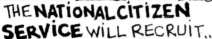

THE NATIONAL CITIZEN SERVICE WILL RECRUIT...

NATIONAL CITIZEN SERVICE

...GANGS OF **SIXTEEN YEAR OLDS** AND **DRILL** THEM IN...

- □ — **TEAMWORK**
- □ — **LEARNING SKILLS**
- □ — **SOCIAL ACTION**
- □ — **GETTING A ROOM** IN A B & B

IT'S ALL **VOLUNTARY** AND... WHERE THE **FACK** DO YOU THINK **YOU'RE GOIN'**?

DON'T IT WARM THE **COCKLES** OF YOUR **FACKIN' 'EART**?

I FINK YOUR **PUSSY** COULD USE A **WALK** MISSUS

NATIONAL CITIZEN SERVICE

OOH, **NO THANKS** SONNY, **NOT RIGHT NOW!**...

I **TELL** YOU WHAT THOUGH, YOU LET TIDDLES GO...

NATIONAL CITIZEN SERVICE

...BECAUSE IT'S TIME FOR ME 'USBAND'S **MANUAL EVACUATION** AND 'E NEEDS A BIT OF A **HAND**!

IS IT THE POLICE, MAUREEN?

NATIONAL CITIZEN SERVICE

WE NEED **SOMETHING BIG**, DAVE. WE NEED...

...A **GAME CHANGER!**

YEAH! RIGHT ON! LET'S PLAY **SCRABBLE!**

NO, I'M AFRAID IT'S SOMETHING **MORE FUNDAMENTAL** WE NEED...

thanks to Keith Flett

DESIGNER STUBBLE!

LOOK – I'M CHANNELING MY ENERGY INTO GROWING MY **DESIGNER STUBBLE!**

IT'S COMING! IT'S COMING!

SOMETIMES I THINK YOU TRY TOO HARD, DAVE

VOTE FOR CHANGE

May 2010

"I'm not a man of faith,
but my wife is."

Nick Clegg, April 2010

THE FINAL DEBATE

©Steve Bell 2010- 3007·30·4·10-

THERE'S MR **CLEGG**

I'VE BEEN TOLD HE'S **NOT** A NAZI **THIS WEEK**

LET'S **LOVE-BOMB** HIM!

SIR! CAN I **HUG YOUR LEG?**

WHY CAN I NO HAVE A **TOAD** OF MY OWN TO **LOVE-BOMB** ME?

EUGGHH! CLEGG STAINS!

FRANKLY HE'S **LOST** IT!!

THE **ORANGE** TIE KILLED IT FOR ME!

THERE'S **MR BROWN!**

HELLO SIR!

WHY **HELLO, YOUNG TOADS!** I'D **LOVE** TO BE **LOVE-BOMBED** Y' KNOW

SIR, SPEAKING AS A ONE-EYED, FAT, OLD, HALF-CREMATED CORPSE, **HOW** IS THE CAMPAIGN GOING?

AAAARRGH! TOADS WITH **TEETH!**

392

Postscript

Catching a first impression, trying to nail it down. That, in some ways, is the essence of being a political cartoonist, because very first impressions are difficult for the subject to control, and once installed utterly impossible to dislodge. It's the art of the bleeding obvious, but who's to say what that is.

When I first drew David Cameron at a party conference I saw smoothness and a distinct air of plausibility. The former quality so commonplace as to be virtually meaningless, the latter quality so vital for a politician yet so lacking in, to take just two examples, William Hague and Iain Duncan Smith. Yet the more I saw of Cameron, the more his smoothness seemed to develop and encompass all his other features.

His well-upholstered, upper-class plumpness and his big, watery eyes were bound up more and more in his baby-bottom complexion. His smoothness soon seemed to take on an other-worldly quality, a kind of androgynous sleekness that accompanied his transformation of the erstwhile 'Nasty Party' into the Sunshine, Springtime and Fluffy Cloud Party.

Cameron's first conference as leader, Bournemouth 2006

Yet he and his even younger chum George were turning into a formidably effective political double act. Despite having all the visual gravitas of a pair of man boobs, the two of them, politically, ran rings around Gordon Brown. Then came the prolonged expenses scandal and Cameron's energetic protestations of complete transparency. The only fully transparent organism that I could think of was a jellyfish; either that or, what was it about those odd folds of skin from his ear to his neck? A balloon that's been twisted.

This January the Tories' first election billboard appeared, with Cameron's supposedly airbrushed face looming large on the left. But I knew, having inspected him at close quarters, that he really was that smooth. He was going to cut the deficit, not the NHS. Total moral opportunism combined with a complete, engorged and erectile sense of his own responsibility. Thus it was that the condom unrolled over his smooth head. It seemed so perfect and so apt, to me at least, and so after some initial opposition (the editor didn't get it), I elected to run with it.

Top left: Cameron, Tory conference 2004. Top right: Tory conference 2006.
Middle: Tory Manifesto launch, April 2010. Bottom left: Tory conference 2008.
Bottom right: 3rd Leader's debate, April 2010

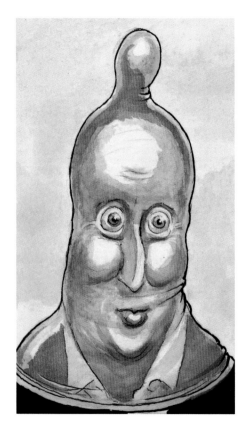

During the general election campaign, which I followed avidly from as close as I could get from the day of the first manifesto launch to the bitter end, I managed to follow David Cameron on his insane, 36 hour, nightworker-bothering dash southwards from East Renfrewshire. My colleague Alex Healey and I accidentally encountered him that evening at a service station between Glasgow and Carlisle. We were enjoying a well-deserved burger and he had nipped in to buy something. I knew it was him, he knew it was me.

He came over to talk, which is strange because I'd never spoken to him before. Unfortunately the camera was locked in the car, so this is the only record I have of the encounter. We shook hands. He asked me:

"The condom … where does that come from?"

A dozen things passed through my mind, like: "They have machines in places like this…" I thought for a moment. What I said was:

"It's to do with the smoothness of your complexion…"

Guardian Comment page cartoon, 12 January 2010

Though actually at the time his face was looking a little raw. He seemed genuinely interested and claimed to have enjoyed the one I'd drawn of him in that day's paper as a large sausage on a butcher's weighing machine.

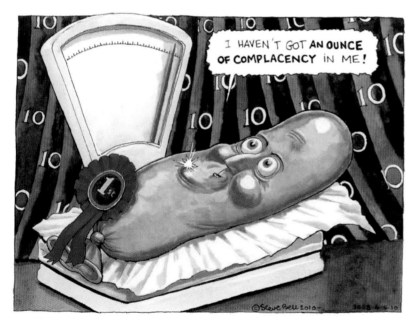

Guardian Comment page cartoon, 4 May 2010

I said he wasn't supposed to. I ventured to ask him what drugs he was on for this lunatic marathon. He laughed and said he'd just bought a Patricia Cornwell book to put himself to sleep on the bus.

Then he was away and we made our separate ways to his photo opportunity with an impressive halibut in a grey and fishy new dawn on a stinking Grimsby fish dock, where I gave up the chase. I had a kip and drove home to bed, and he went on to victory by the skin of his... but that's enough of that.

48 HOURS ON THE GO AND STILL FRESH AS A DAISY

Guardian Comment page cartoon, 6 May 2010